The Virtue of
Generosity

The Elves and the Shoemaker

Adapted by Jennifer Boudart
Illustrated by Kristen Goeters
Cover illustrated by Angela Jarecki

ISBN: 0-7853-7304-7

Copyright © 2002 Publications International, Ltd.

D1021479

One harsh winter, a poor shoemaker and his wife discovered that they had only enough leather left to make one pair of shoes. After the leather was gone, they would have no way to make a living, for they could not afford any more.

"Things will work out," the shoemaker said. He cut the leather and went to bed, planning to finish the shoes the next day.

In the morning, instead of the pieces of leather, the shoemaker found a marvelous pair of shoes! The shoes were beautifully made, with fantastic detail. "Who could have made these?" he wondered, amazed.

The shoemaker and his wife marveled at the shoes. They knew such fine shoes would bring a good price.

At that moment a traveler walked into the shop. "I have been walking throughout the countryside," he said, "and my travels have worn holes in my shoes. I was hoping that I could buy a pair from you."

The traveler tried on the new shoes, and they fit perfectly. He walked around the shop for a few moments and said, "These are the most comfortable shoes I've ever worn!" Then he gave the shoemaker a shiny gold coin to pay for them.

With the gold coin the shoemaker bought enough leather to make two pairs of shoes. Once again the shoemaker cut the leather into pieces and placed them on his workbench. The next morning he found two more pairs of finished shoes.

Within hours the shoemaker sold both pairs of shoes and bought more leather. The next day there were four pairs of shoes waiting on the workbench. This continued for many nights, until the shoemaker's shelves were filled with the most beautiful shoes anyone had ever seen. The shoemaker and his wife soon became very prosperous.

But something was still bothering the shoemaker. "Every night, someone works hard to help us," he said to his wife, "but we don't even know who it is. Why don't we stay up to find out?"

That night the shoemaker cut the leather into pieces and placed them on his workbench. But instead of going to bed, he and his wife hid in the doorway.

The moon rose and filled the room with silver light. Soon something was moving on the workbench. Two elves were there! They stood just a few inches tall, no taller than the exquisite shoe they were sewing.

The next morning the shoemaker and his wife looked at the newly made shoes, and thought about the elves. "Did you see how quickly and carefully those little fellows worked?" asked the shoemaker.

His wife frowned and answered, "I only saw their ragged clothing and bare feet. Clearly they are in great need, yet they work all night—every night!—to help us."

Her husband had an idea. "We'll make those little elves the clothes and shoes they need! They're so tiny that it will be easy."

The couple started right away to make the two tiny suits of clothing.

That evening, instead of leaving pieces of leather on the bench, they left new clothes and shoes. They hid behind the doorway and waited for the elves to come.

The elves appeared at midnight. They climbed upon the workbench, then stopped in their tracks. Where were the pieces of leather and the tools? The elves were amazed when they saw the clothes. At once they put on the fine new suits. They were so excited they began to dance.

The shoemaker and his wife were so pleased they could hardly keep themselves from cheering!

Weeks passed, and the shoemaker's shop was always filled with people. He still offered the finest shoes in the land.

One thing had changed, though. The elves had not come back since the night they received their new clothes. But the shoemaker and his wife did not mind. They were just glad to have helped the elves.

As the years passed, the shoemaker and his wife often thought about the two elves. Because of their kindness and generosity, the shoemaker and his wife lived happily. Their cupboards were always filled, and their house was always warm.

Generosity

Generosity is about giving to others without thinking of yourself. The elves were generous with their time and talents, working hard and not expecting anything in return.

The shoemaker and his wife responded to the elves' generosity by showing their appreciation. Being generous to others can be rewarding, in more ways than one.